Series consultant: Dr Dorothy Rowe

The author and publisher would like to thank the
staff and pupils of the following schools for their help
in the making of this book: St Barnabas Church of
England Primary School, Pimlico; Kenmont Primary
School, Hammersmith & Fulham; St Vincent de Paul
Roman Catholic School, Westminster; Mayfield
Primary School, Cambridge; St Peter's Church of
England Primary School, Sible Hedingham.

A CIP catalogue record for this book is available from
the British Library.

ISBN 0-7136-6078-3

First paperback edition published 2001
First published in hardback in 1997 by
A & C Black (Publishers) Ltd,
37 Soho Square, London, W1D 3QZ

Printed in Hong Kong through Colorcraft Ltd.

CHOICES

Being Friends

Althea

Photographs by
Charlie Best

Illustrations by
Conny Jude

A & C Black · London

What is a friend?

A friend is a person who you can trust, someone who you care about and who cares about you.

They put up with you when you are grumpy or miserable.

My friends make me laugh.

Our friends may be very
different from each other.
Some friends may be
full of energy and
fun to be with.

I like Tom,
he makes me laugh.
He never stops
talking!

Other friends are good to talk to
when you have problems.

Rubia is much
quieter than Tom.
She listens to me.

Some people prefer to have a large group of friends.
They feel it's important to like lots of people and
for lots of people to like them. They might even
worry if they think someone doesn't like them.

Other people feel happier with one or two close friends.
They don't worry too much about how many
other people like them.

Do you have a best friend?
Best friends are the friends
that you feel closest to.

I used to get teased when I was younger, so I know what it's like.

When people tease me, my best friend sticks up for me.

You can still get angry and fight with a best friend. But because you care so much about each other, you'll probably make it up soon.

We didn't speak for a week, but now we're back together again.

Your family can be friends, too.

Brothers and sisters often find it difficult to like each other all the time. But most people find that their family support them when they are sad or need help.

They hug me when I'm feeling miserable.

Have you got any grown-up friends?
Sometimes you may find it easy to talk
to someone who is a lot older
than you.

"Mum has a friend
and when she comes
to stay with us,
I talk to her a lot.
She's really good
at helping me
sort out
problems."

When a group of friends
gets together, it can
be a lot of fun.
It can make
you feel good
to belong
to a group.

But sometimes, people do things in a group which they wouldn't do on their own. A group might gang up on someone and not let them join in with a game. Groups of people can tease or bully a person on their own.

Ramona says, "I thought Alice liked me, but when she's with the others, she's different. Sometimes, she starts picking on me."

They call you chicken if you don't do what they say.

As you grow older, you'll probably change the way you feel about people and things. Even best friends can change.

"I went on holiday last term and when I came back, Paul was best friends with someone else. I think he was jealous because I had been on holiday."

You may feel very hurt if a close friend changes and makes friends with someone else. It can be hard at first, but it doesn't always mean that you have to stop being friends with them.

I felt jealous when Zoe made friends with Alice, but now the three of us are friends.

Sometimes, people need to have time on their own.
It doesn't mean that they're lonely, they may just
need to be alone for a while. When do you
spend time apart from others?

Peter says, "I like writing stories and
painting pictures, but I need to be on
my own to really concentrate on them.
I don't want to spend all my time
with other people, even my friends."

"I didn't exactly break up with my best friend, but I needed some time away from him to see other people. I know he was a bit upset, but we still play together sometimes."

Sometimes, people find it hard to make friends.
They might feel lonely and left out when
they see other people enjoying
themselves.

I wish I could play

Perhaps they haven't noticed
there are other people who
are lonely too. Those people
might welcome the chance to
make friends, even if they're
too shy to say so.

If you are trying to make new friends, it's not
always best to choose the most popular children.
It may not be easy to get to know them well
if they already have
lots of friends.

Do you know anyone who does things
just so that people will like them?

Anna's always
showing off because
she wants to be
popular.

You don't have to be
friends with everyone.
It's up to you to choose
who you really like.
We're all different and
we can't expect to like
and be liked by everyone.

Some people find it difficult to make friends because they think other people won't like them.

We all need to learn to like ourselves - then other people are more likely to care about us too.

We may not always understand our friends, but that doesn't stop us from liking them.

We can learn a lot about someone by being their friend.

Getting to know someone well as a friend can teach us a lot about ourselves. If you don't mind what your best friend looks like, you might stop worrying about how you look yourself.

Whether you are close to one person or lots of people, friends help give you more confidence to be yourself.

For teachers and parents

A note from Dorothy Rowe

Parents and teachers know that children can often experience problems with friendships. But they sometimes forget that in order to help, they must first find out how the child sees the problem. A child won't see the situation in the same way as an adult because no two people ever see things in exactly the same way.

Remembering this, an adult won't say to themselves, 'I know what is wrong with the child', but will explore possible reasons for the child's behaviour: for example, 'Does this child have difficulty in making friends?', or 'Is this a child who would prefer to have one good friend rather than lots of friends?'.

It's possible to think up dozens of alternative reasons as answers to the question, 'Why does this child behave like this?'. Doing so helps the adult to ask better questions. However, the answer can only come from the child.

We make and lose friends throughout our lives. Parents and teachers should be prepared to talk to children about their own difficulties and experiences in dealing with friendship, and not pretend to provide easy solutions to the problems which children encounter in this area. This way the adult and the child can explore the dilemma together.

People have different expectations from friends. To start a discussion and get everyone involved, you could begin by compiling a list of qualities which are significant in friendship; then you and the children could place them in order of importance. Compare your answers and ask why the children feel that certain qualities are the most important in a friend. Examples might include:

• A friend is someone you can trust; someone who will keep your secrets and won't tell them to other people.

• A friend puts up with you even when you are bad tempered.

• A friend sticks up for you when other people are being nasty to you.

• Friends don't gossip or tell tales about you behind your back.

• Friends make you feel happy; you can completely relax with a friend.

When going through the book again it may be useful to discuss some of the following points with the children:

Pages 4-5 Some people are willing to be a friend when everything is going well for you, but don't support you when you need comfort or help. They are sometimes called 'fair-weather friends'.

Page 8 It's important to judge for yourself who you want to be friends with, and not to be swayed by other people's opinions. Some friends may have greater difficulties than having to wear glasses, or being the shortest in the class. It can take courage to stick up for them if they are being teased or picked on.

Page 9 How do different children make up after a row? If an argument develops into a feud, it may become very difficult to make up.

Page 13 Children who do not generally bully other children may find themselves doing things they are ashamed of when they are part of a group.

Page 15 What does it feel like to be jealous of someone? What has made you jealous of people in the past?

Page 16 Some people need to have time on their own to sort out their feelings. It is important that others do not take this as a slight.

Page 18 Some people find it easy to make friends. People often worry so much about themselves and their own feelings that they don't notice other people who need friends.

New situations can be scary, so we need to make new people feel welcome. You shouldn't judge someone by how they behave at first, because people sometimes act oddly when they are scared or shy.

Further reading

Children may find it interesting and helpful to have a look at some of the following story books which also deal with the subject of being friends.

Charles Ashton
Ruth and the Blue Horse
(Walker, 1995)

Annie Dalton
Tilly Beany and the Best Friend Machine
(Mammoth, 1997)

Paula Danziger
Amber Brown is not a Crayon
(Macmillan, 1994)

Mary Hooper
Best Friends, Worst Luck
(Walker, 1993)

Gene Kemp
The Turbulent Term of Tyke Tiler
(Puffin, 1994)

Bryan Newton
Friends and Enemies
(HarperCollins, 1995)